GWIL GARW

a'r Carchar Crisial

GWIL GARW

a'r Carchar Crisial

GAN
HUW AARON

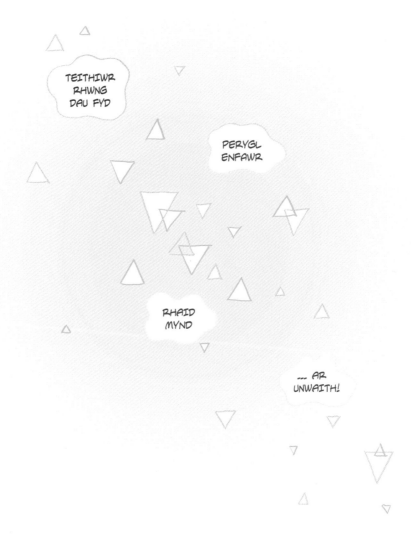

i Luned

Argraffiad cyntaf 2021,
Ail argraffiad 2022
© testun a lluniau: Huw Aaron, 2021

Cynhyrchwyd y gyfrol hon gyda chymorth ariannol Cyngor Llyfrau Cymru,
a chyhoeddwyd y stori yn wreiddiol yng nghomic *Mellten*, gan y Lolfa.

Rhif llyfr rhyngwladol:
9781914303036

Cyhoeddwyd yng Nghymru gan Llyfrau Broga, Yr Eglwys Newydd

DIOGEL. FFIW. ROEDD HYNNA'N AGOS.

?!

HELÔ ETO.

Y LLEIDR! WNEI DI DDIM DIANC ETO! MAE'R GOSB AM DDWYN BAEDD YN LLYM.

OND SUT OEDDECH CHI'N GWYBOD BLE O'N I?

FE WNAETH ADERYN BACH SÔN EFALLAI Y BYDDAI RHYWBETH YN HWYLIO I LAWR YR AFON ATON NI.

WEL, DYNA GYFLEUS. AT Y BRENIN RYDYN NI'N DY GYMRYD DI....

ER MWYN IDDO DORRI DY BEN I FFWRDD.

PERFFAITH!

O, DIAR.

GRR! Y CORRACH BLIN. O'N I'N GWYBOD BOD 'NA FFORDD GYFLYMACH I'R LLYS.

Y LLYS! HEI! GADEWCH FI I FYND! MAE'N RHAID I MI ROI NEGES BWYSIG I'R BRENIN!

DYNA GYLLELL NEIS, GYDA LLAW. SGLEINIOG.

HAEARN, WEDI EI GLODDIO O GALON MYNYDD A'I BERFFEITHIO YN Y TÂN. EFFEITHIOL IAWN YN ERBYN BWBACHOD, ELLYLLOD... A THYLWYTH TEG.

!!!

HMM. LYFLI. NOS DA.

NOS DA... GWIL GARW.

YN Y CYFAMSER...

PA MOR BELL I'R DDINAS RŴAN, CORRACH?

DDIM YN BELL NAWR, DDERWYDD.

WEDI'R LLANNERCH NESAF, WNAWN NI GYRRAEDD Y NOD.

GOBEITHIO HYNNY - MAE AMSER YN BRIN.

TRWY FAN HYN -

O.

IAWCS!

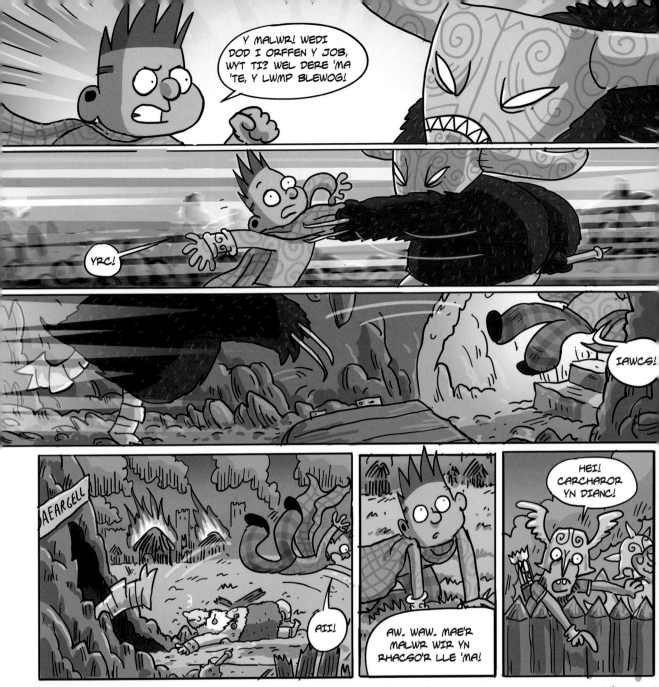

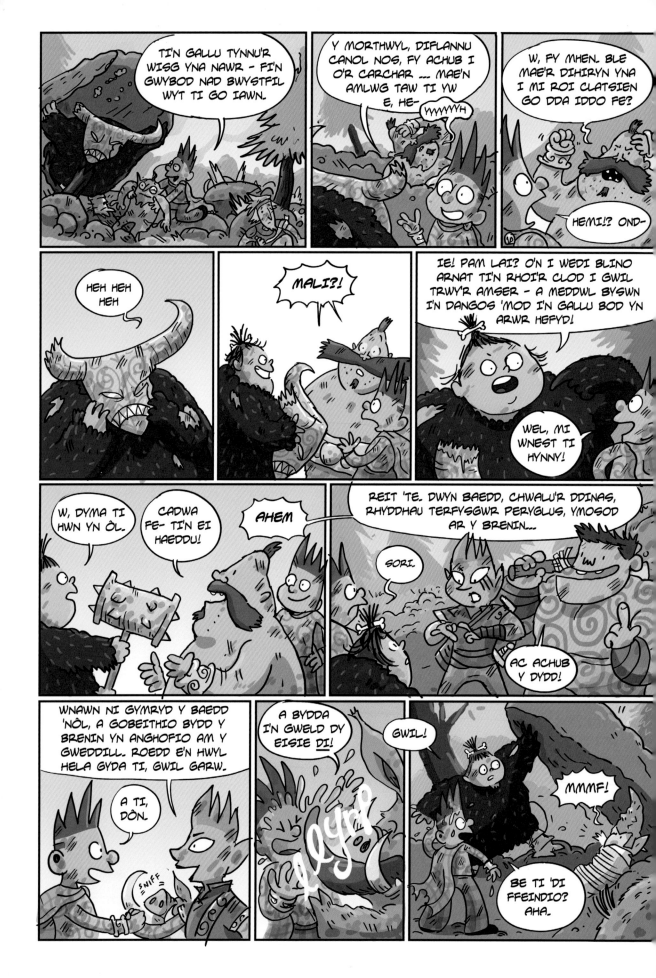

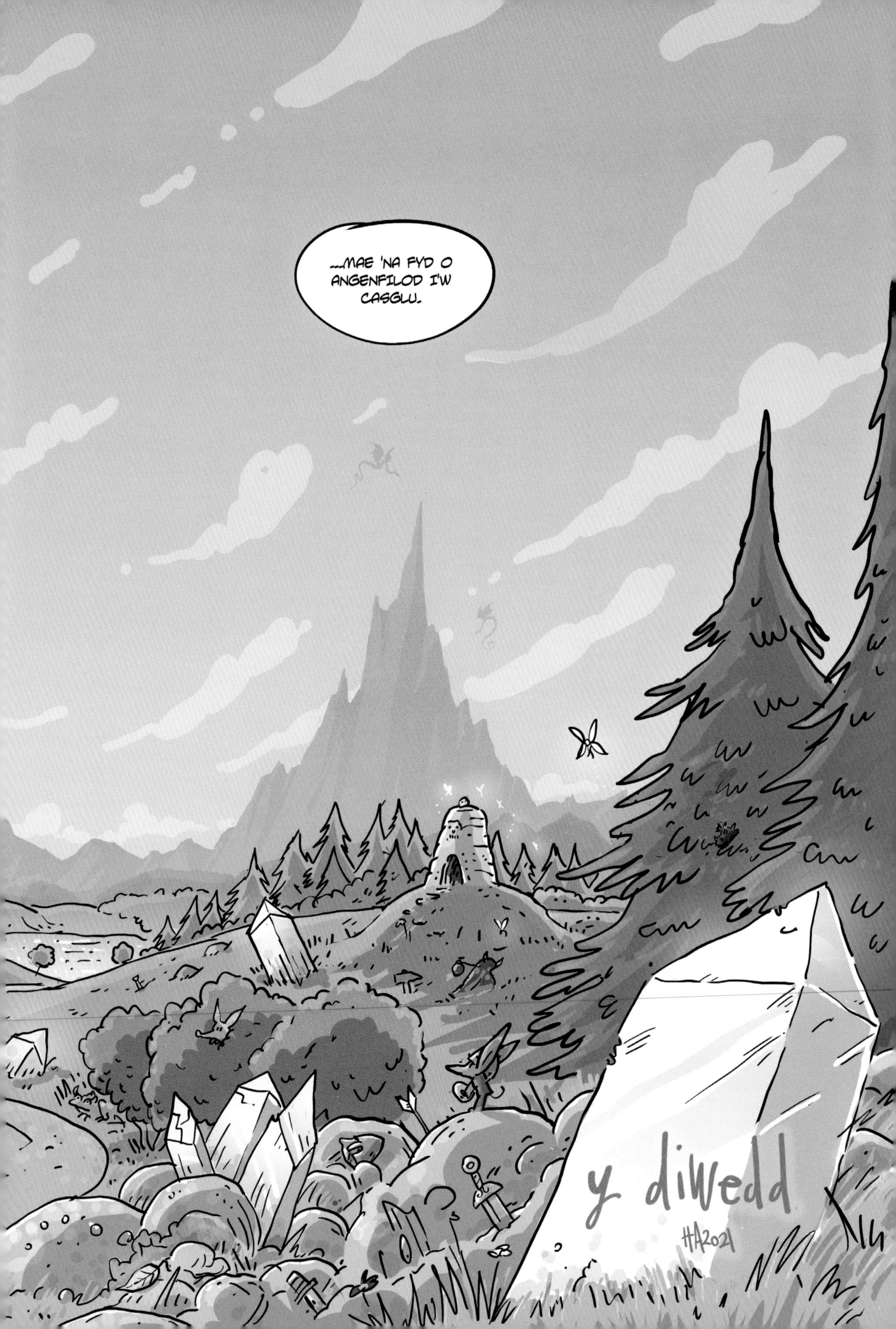
...MAE 'NA FYD O ANGENFILOD I'W CASGLU.
y diwedd
HA2021

Wedi joio? Beth am ddarllen y comics anhygoel yma gan Llyfrau Broga hefyd!

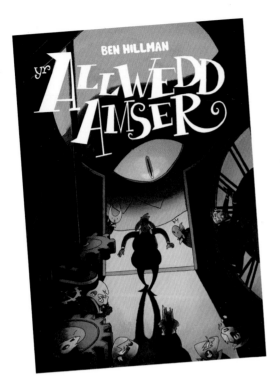

Yr Allwedd Amser
gan Ben Hillman

Mae Nefyn a Trefor yn darganfod allwedd sy'n agor drysau i lefydd anhygoel, ac yn camu i antur fwyaf eu bywyd. Mae'r bydysawd ac amser ei hun yn y fantol - a Nefyn a Trefor ydi'r arwyr lleiaf addas ar gyfer y dasg!

Ydy'r ffrindiau dewr yn gallu atal y byd rhag cael ei rwygo'n ddarnau? Nofel graffig llawn antur, hiwmor a gwaith celf anhygoel.

Addas i oed 7-12, £6.99.

Rali'r Gofod 4002
gan Joe Watson

Mae cystadleuaeth Cwpan Manta 4002 ar fin cychwyn! Mae tymor o rasio cyffrous o'n blaenau, gyda thîm annisgwyl o'r blaned Cymru Newydd yn ymuno am y tro cyntaf.

All Iola brofi ei gwerth fel peilot? All ei chriw rhyfedd stopio dadlau yn ddigon hir i ennill ras? A beth yw'r cynlluniau tywyll sy'n ffrwtian yn y cysgodion?

Addas i oed 7-12, £6.99.

BROGA

meet the
ambulance crew

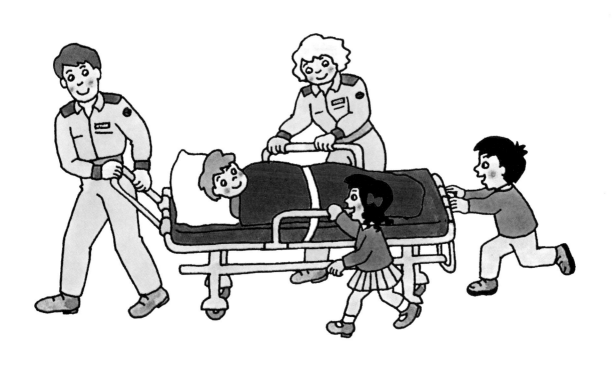

When Topsy and Tim arrived at school,
they saw a big, white ambulance standing
in the school playground.
'Oh dear,' said Mummy. 'I hope there
hasn't been an accident.'
'It's all right Mum,' said Tim. 'We're
going to learn all about the Ambulance
Service today. That's why the ambulance
is here.'

The twins ran to tell their teacher that the ambulance had arrived and saw two strangers in their classroom. Topsy and Tim guessed they were the ambulance crew.

'Dave and Nicky have come to
tell us all about their work,' said
Miss Terry. 'Dave is a Paramedic and
Nicky is an Ambulance Technician.
They are trained to help people, a bit like
doctors and nurses.'

Everyone sat down to listen to Dave
and Nicky tell them about the
Ambulance Service.
'Let's start at the beginning,' said
Dave. 'I want one of you children
to pretend to have an accident.'

Andy Anderson pretended to fall off
a chair. 'OW, OW, OW!' he cried.
'Andy's hurt! He's broken his leg,'
said Topsy.
'And his arm,' said Tim.
'Andy needs to get to hospital quickly,'
said Nicky. 'Does anyone know how to
phone for an ambulance?'

'I do,' said Louise Lewis. 'My mummy
taught me.' Louise rang 999 on the
toy telephone.
'Hello,' she said. 'Please send an
ambulance to Hatcham School.
Andy has fallen off a chair
and broken his leg and his arm.'

'Ambulance Control tells us where
to go,' said Dave, 'so we can get there
as quickly as possible.'
He knelt down and felt Andy's leg.
'This leg is broken,' he said.
'His arm is broken too.
We need splints and a stretcher.'
Nicky hurried out to the ambulance
to get them.

'If Andy's leg and arm are hurt very badly we would let him breathe some special gas to stop the pain,' said Technician Nicky. She took a little mask out of a blue bag and showed Andy how to put it on.

Paramedic Dave put a splint on
Andy's leg and a sling on his arm.
'These will keep Andy's arm and leg
steady and comfortable on the way
to hospital,' explained Dave.

Nicky and Dave tucked Andy up
on the stretcher and wheeled him
out to the ambulance. Miss Terry
and all the children followed and
watched them lift the stretcher
into the ambulance. Andy looked
very comfortable.

'You can all come and look inside
the ambulance,' called Dave, 'but
there isn't room for everyone at
once.' Miss Terry divided the class
into two groups. The first group
climbed the ambulance steps
and went inside.

Topsy and Tim were in the second group, so they had to wait outside. They ran around the playground shouting 'Nee-nor, nee-nor, nee-nor.' 'Steady, children,' said Miss Terry. 'We're ambulances hurrying to an accident,' said Topsy.

At last the first group came out.
Andy came out too. Now it was the
turn of Topsy and Tim's group to go
into the ambulance. They climbed
up the big steps and went in.

The ambulance was full of all sorts
of interesting things.
'This special blue Trauma light is
for patients who can't look at bright
lights,' said Dave. 'It shows up bruises
too.' Topsy had a bruise on her leg.
The blue light showed it up well.

There were cupboards full of useful
things all around the ambulance.
Kerry tried on an oxygen mask.
A little red ball in a tube measured
the oxygen she was breathing.

'We all need oxygen to stay alive,'
 said Nicky. 'There is plenty in the air,
but sometimes, when people are ill,
they need extra.'
Vinda and Tony took turns to measure
their oxygen levels by putting a special
clip on their fingers. A screen
told them how much they had.

Tim saw another screen.
'Is that a TV?' he asked.
'No,' said Dave. 'It's a Heart Monitor.
It shows a picture of your heartbeat.
If you were very ill and your heart
stopped beating we would try
to start it again.'

Nicky turned a Suction Unit on and
Stevie felt it suck at his hand.
'This is to stop people choking,' said
Nicky. 'It's like the sucking tube the
dentist puts in your mouth.'

Two brightly coloured jackets were
hanging up behind the front seats.
'We wear these when we go to road
accidents, so that the traffic can see
us easily,' said Dave. Topsy and Tim
tried the yellow jackets on.
'They're a bit big!' said Topsy.

Suddenly a voice said, 'Control
to Nicky and Dave. I have an
emergency for you.' It was the
Ambulance Controller speaking on
the radio.
'Hello, Control,' said Dave into the
mike. 'We will be on our way
as quickly as possible.'

Miss Terry helped the children
out of the ambulance. Topsy
and Tim were the last to leave.
'Are you going to turn on the siren
and flashing lights?' asked Tim.
'Would you and Topsy like to do
it for us?' asked Nicky.
'Yes please,' said Topsy and Tim.
Nicky let Topsy press the button
for the flashing lights. Tim pressed
the button for the siren.

The ambulance drove out of the
school playground with blue lights
flashing and siren sounding. It
was very noisy. The children shouted
'THANK YOU!' and waved goodbye.
'I'm going to be a Paramedic and
help people when I grow up,' said
Topsy.
'Me, too,' said Tim.

meet the firefighters

One morning when Topsy and Tim
were on their way to school, they
heard a fire engine coming.

It raced past them, sirens sounding and blue lights flashing. All the other traffic got out of the way. Everyone knew that the firefighters were hurrying to put out a fire.

'Kerry's dad is a firefighter,' said
Topsy. 'I expect he is on that fire
engine.'

But Kerry's dad was not on the
fire engine. It was his morning
off and he was taking Kerry to
school. Topsy and Tim told him
about the fire engine they had seen.
'They're called fire appliances, not
fire engines,' said Kerry.

'There's an open day at my
fire station on Saturday,' said
Kerry's dad. 'Would you like to
come and see all our fire appliances?'
'Yes, please,' said Topsy and Tim.
On Saturday Topsy and Tim
and Mummy set out for
Bellford Fire Station.

There were lots of children at
the fire station. Firefighters in
yellow helmets were looking after
them. Topsy and Tim soon found
Kerry and her dad.

Kerry was waiting to go up on
a long turntable ladder. Topsy
and Tim wanted to go up too.
A firefighter helped them all
into a cage on the end of
the ladder. He gave them
safety helmets to wear.

A firefighter at the
back of the appliance
pulled a lever and the
ladder started to go up.

It grew longer and longer and
went higher and higher, until
the people on the ground looked
as small as toys.
'We hose water down on to burning
buildings from up here,' said
the firefighter.
'And you rescue people from high
windows and roofs,' said Kerry.

When they came down from the ladder
Mummy bought them each a little
firefighter's helmet.
'I'm going to be a firefighter
when I grow up,' said Kerry.
'Can girls be firefighters?' asked Topsy.
'I don't think so,' said Tim.

'Yes, they can!' said the lady
who was selling the toy helmets.
'I'm a firefighter, just like Kerry's
dad. Women can be firefighters, but
they have to be as strong and as
brave as the men.'
To show how strong she was, she gave
Tim a fireman's lift.

Kerry's dad took them to see
how the fire station worked.
'When there is a fire and someone
phones 999,' he said, 'we get
the message on a teleprinter.
A loudspeaker tells us where to go
and which appliances to take.'

'Alarm bells ring and the firefighters
run to the appliances. If they are
upstairs they slide down a pole.
It's quicker than running down the
stairs.'

Kerry's dad lifted the children
into the cab of a big fire appliance.
They pretended to drive to a fire.

Near the big fire appliance
was a much smaller one.
'Is that a baby fire engine?'
asked Tim.
'It's a van full of rescue equipment,'
said Kerry's dad. 'We take it to
accidents and rescue people from
crashed cars and trucks.'

Kerry's dad showed them the tall
tower where the firefighters practised
with their ladders and hoses.
'When we have finished we hang
the hoses in the tower to dry,'
he told them.

Next to the tower was a room
that had been on fire. It made
their noses tickle.
'We make smoky fires in there,'
said Kerry's dad. 'Then we practise
putting them out and rescuing people.
We have to wear masks and carry tanks
of air on our backs, or we would choke.'

Kerry took Topsy and Tim into
a showroom full of
fire dangers. It looked like
an ordinary living room.
'See if you can spot where
fires could start,' said Kerry.
Tim spotted a cigarette on an
armchair seat.
'That could start a fire,' he said.

Topsy spotted a box of matches
on the floor.
'A naughty little child might start
a fire with those,' she said.
'And that electric heater should
be behind a fireguard,' said Mummy.

Mummy spotted more fire dangers
near a kitchen stove.
'Are smoke-detectors any use?'
she asked Kerry's dad. 'I think
I ought to get one.'

Kerry's dad showed them a smoke-
detector and made it work. It
made loud BLEEP-BLEEP-BLEEP noises.
'If there was a fire in your home
one night, the smoke-detector
would wake you up,' he said.
'We've got one,' Kerry told Topsy.

It was time to go home, but
before they went, Kerry's dad
gave them one last treat.
It was a ride round the
fire station yard on a
children's fire appliance.
The clever firefighters had
made it specially for their
open day.

meet the police

One morning Topsy and Tim were
in a great hurry to get to school.
'The police are coming to talk
to us today,' they told Mummy.

When they reached school a
police car was already there.
A policeman and a policewoman
got out.
'Can anyone tell us where to find
Miss Terry?' they asked.
'Why? What's she done?' said
Andy Anderson.

Topsy and Tim knew where
to find Miss Terry.
'Miss Terry is our teacher,'
they said.

'Police Constable Webb and Woman
Police Constable May have come
to tell us all about the work
that the police do,' said Miss Terry.
'Do any of you children know the
jobs that the police do?'

'They catch burglars,' said Andy Anderson.
'They look after traffic,' said Tim.
'They find you when you are lost,'
said Topsy.
'Yes, we do all those things,'
said PC Webb, 'and we look after
lost things as well as lost children.'

'Suppose Tim was walking down
the street,' said PC Webb, 'and
he found a purse full of money
on the ground. What should he do?'
'Spend it?' said Andy Anderson.
'No,' said PC Webb. 'That would
be very wrong. He should take it
to a police station.'

'Suppose Topsy was the one who
had lost the purse,' said WPC May.
'What should she do?'
None of the children knew.
'She should go to the police station
and tell them she had lost her purse,'
said WPC May. 'Then the police
would be able to give it back to her.'

WPC May asked Topsy and Tim
to help her pin up some pictures
of the police at work.
One of the pictures showed a police dog.
'Have you got a police dog?' asked Topsy.

'No,' said WPC May. 'Police dogs
belong to police dog handlers.
The dogs are trained to find
things that are lost or hidden.
They are very clever.'

PC Webb told the children that
one of the most important jobs
the police do is to come into
schools and talk to children
about safety.
'Some places are dangerous to play in,'
he said.

The children helped PC Webb
think of some dangerous places.
'Don't play near deep water —
you might fall in,' said Kerry.
'Don't play by a railway line —
a train might hit you,' said
little Stevie Dunton.
'Don't play on a building site —
you could cut yourself on something
sharp and rusty,' said Louise Lewis.

'Always stay where your mother can keep an eye on you,' said PC Webb, 'and never ever talk to strangers. If a stranger tries to talk to you in the street or anywhere else, don't let them come near you.'
'What is a stranger?' asked Tim.

'A stranger is someone you don't know,'
said PC Webb. 'Most people are
good and kind, but there are some
people who like to take children
away and hurt them.
So NEVER get into a stranger's car —
even if they know your name and seem
nice and friendly.'

'If a stranger has tried to talk
to you, or asked you to get in
his car, tell your mummy or your
teacher and they should tell the
police,' said PC Webb.

WPC May helped the children
act a play called Stranger-Danger.
Andy Anderson was a bad stranger.
'Will you help me find my
lost puppy?' he said to Vinda.
'No!' shouted Vinda, keeping
out of his way.

Rai was Vinda's daddy.
He took Vinda to the police station
to see WPC Topsy and PC Tim.
'My little girl says a stranger
frightened her,' said Rai.
'Thank you for telling us,' said Tim.
'We will try and catch that bad man.'

After the play it was time for
PC Webb and WPC May to go back
to their police station.
The children waved goodbye.

On their way home from school
that day Topsy saw something shiny
on the pavement. It was a very
pretty brooch.
'Someone will be sad to have lost
such a nice brooch,' said Mummy.

'We must take it to the police
station,' said Tim. 'Then the police
can give it back to the person
who lost it.'

'Hello,' said the desk sergeant in
the police station. 'Can I help you?'
'Topsy's found a pretty brooch,'
said Tim. The desk sergeant took
the brooch and wrote about it
in her book. She wrote down Topsy
and Tim's address too.
'We will let you know if we find
the owner,' she said.

They went home and were having tea
when the phone rang. Dad answered it.
It was the police to say that they
had found the owner of the lost brooch.
'I wonder who it belonged to?' said
Mummy.

That night, when Topsy and Tim
were getting ready for bed, there
was a knock at the door. It was
Mrs Higley-Pigley.
'Thank you, Topsy and Tim,' she said,
'for finding my very special brooch
and for taking it to the police.'